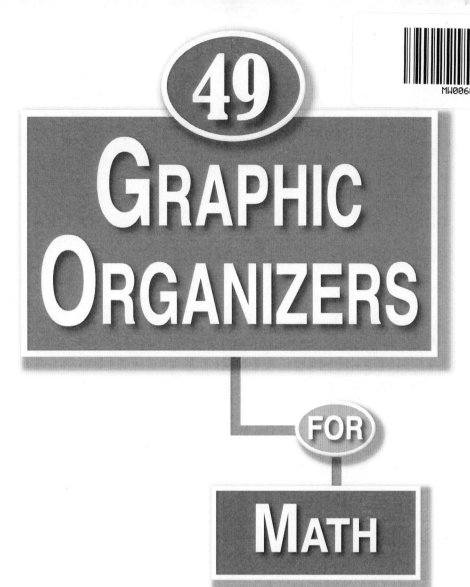

49 GRAPHIC ORGANIZERS FOR MATH

Sunflower
education

*Exceptional Books for Teachers
and Parents*

Illustrators   Fian Arroyo
Steven Durke

ISBN-13: 978-1-937166-25-0
© 2019 by Sunflower Education.
All rights reserved. Printed in the U.S.A.

Contents

Graphic Organizers

Number and Operations

Algebra

Geometry

Measurement

Data Analysis and Probability

Problem Solving

Contents

Introduction

Graphic organization of information comes naturally to people. It even predates writing. Ancient peoples used a variety of ingenious graphic methods to organize, record, and transmit information for centuries before some of these methods developed into writing. This fact alone seems to indicate that the human mind is well-suited to organizing and interpreting information presented graphically.

Modern psychological and educational research has proved the effectiveness of different visual devices—especially graphic organizers—as powerful communication and learning tools. Indeed, dozens of studies have established that graphic organizers provide students and teachers with numerous benefits.

Benefits for Students

Recent scientific studies have only confirmed what teachers working in the trenches have known for some time: graphic organizers help students. You can ask any teacher with experience using graphic organizers, and he or she will likely identify at least one, and probably several, benefits of graphic organizers for students:

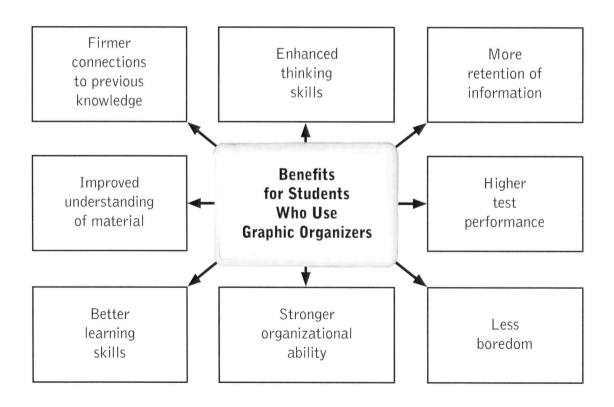

Introduction

Benefits for Teachers

Teachers who use graphic organizers benefit as much as the students. The overriding advantage is that you will elicit better performance from your students. In addition, the following benefits have also been reported:

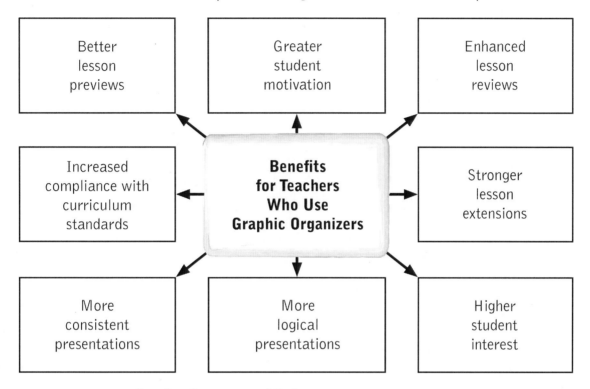

Using *Graphic Organizers: Math*

The graphic organizers in this book were conceived, designed, and organized to maximize their usefulness for both students and teachers. They:

- address fundamental curriculum topics and crucial learning skills, and support essential student learning about mathematics.

- are designed to be visually interesting and academically appropriate. Information is presented in a logical format. In most cases, the graphic organizers are self-explanatory. There is no superfluous information, and there is ample room for students to write in the answer spaces. Form follows function; these graphic organizers direct and enhance student understanding as opposed to clouding it.

- were developed in keeping with the national curriculum standards advocated by the National Council of Teachers of Mathematics. Every graphic organizer meets at least one, and often several, national and state curriculum standards.

Introduction

To assist you in making the most of these graphic organizers, each one is supported in the "Teaching Notes" section with an objective, teaching tips, and discussion questions. These will help you introduce, teach, and extend each graphic organizer.

The graphic organizers can be used as previews, lessons, reviews, or extension activities. They can be assigned as homework or for in-class completion and done by individual students, student pairs, small groups, or the entire class.

You are encouraged to modify these graphic organizers according to your specific classroom needs. For example, you might direct students to add lines and cells to incorporate additional information, or have them cross out parts of a graphic organizer they do not need.

However you choose to use them, you will find the graphic organizers in *Graphic Organizers: Math* an invaluable addition to your teaching resources.

Research and Standards

Decades of research have consistently demonstrated the value of graphic organizers to both teachers and students. Indeed, few other classroom tools have been so widely and highly praised by education researchers, and so uniformly declared a "best practice."

Education professor Gloria A. Dye (2000) summarized the benefits of graphic organizers:

> Graphic organizers can benefit teachers, students, and parents. By using graphic organizers, teachers can have a clear understanding of what they want to address in their classes. Graphic organizers provide students with a road map to follow as they expand their schemas by linking them to existing knowledge. When looking at a graphic organizer ... parents can have a clearer view of what their children will learn or what they have learned in a content-area class. By serving as a means of helping students link the new information with their existing knowledge base, graphic organizers can contribute to our ultimate goal—student learning.

Research and Standards

Specifically, studies have established that graphic organizers:

- work at every grade level;
- are useful at every step of the teaching cycle;
- augment teacher effectiveness;
- apply to students of all ability levels, including those with special needs;
- promote both comprehension and higher-order thinking skills;
- improve decision-making;
- enhance reading comprehension; and
- sharpen research skills.

Meeting National Standards

Graphic Organizers: Math supports the authoritative national education standards put forth by the National Council of Teachers of Mathematics (NCTM) in its *Principles and Standards for School Mathematics.* These standards are (NCTM, 2000):

Content Standards
- Number and Operations
- Algebra
- Geometry
- Measurement
- Data Analysis and Probability

Process Standards
- Problem Solving
- Reasoning and Proof
- Communication
- Connections
- Representation

The structure of *Graphic Organizers: Math* reflects this presentation, and each activity supports a specific topic within a content/process standard.

Baxendell, B. (2003, January-February). Consistent, coherent, creative: The 3 c's of graphic organizers. *Teaching Exceptional Children, 35,* 46–53.

Dye, G. (2000, January-February). Graphic organizers to the rescue! Helping students link—and remember—information. *Teaching Exceptional Children, 32,* 72–76.

Egan, M. (1999, May). Reflections on effective use of graphic organizers. *Journal of Adolescent & Adult Literacy, 42,* 641–645.

Katayama, A. & Robinson, D. (2000, Winter). Getting students 'partially' involved in note-taking using graphic organizers. *Journal of Experimental Education, 68,* 119–133.

Kealy, W. (2000, Fall). The role of semantic congruency in the design of graphic organizers. *Quarterly Review of Distance Education, 1,* 205–214.

National Council of Teachers of Mathematics. (2000). *Principles and standards for school mathematics.* Reston, VA: Author.

Teaching Notes

Number and Operations

1. Types of Numbers (page 1)

Objective

Students will identify and investigate different types of numbers and their use in the media and everyday life.

Teaching Tips

This graphic organizer works well as a whole-class activity. Direct students to look for examples of how different types of numbers are used in their daily lives (on TV shows, in magazines, in conversations, etc.).

Discussion Questions

- What are the different types of numbers?

- When is each different type of number used?

- Why is it important to be able to recognize numbers by type?

2. Large Numbers (page 2)

Objective

Students will identify the name and exponential and numerical expressions of large numbers.

Teaching Tips

This graphic organizer works well as a partners activity. Emphasize the importance of understanding scientific notation for use in other areas. Consider directing students to dictionaries to find the etymology or word origin of several of the number words.

Discussion Questions

- What is the scientific notation for each number?

- What are the numerical forms for million through nonillion?

- How is the number of zeroes in a large number related to its scientific notation?

- How can knowing word parts help you identify large numbers?

Teaching Notes

3. Equivalencies of Fractions, Decimals, and Percents (page 3)

Objective

Students will demonstrate an understanding of the equivalencies of fractions, decimals, and percents and convert from one form to another.

Teaching Tips

Consider having students find three examples of fractions, decimals, and percents in the newspaper and convert each one to the other two types. Ask students to explain why the numbers were expressed that way.

Discussion Questions

- Does every fraction have an equivalent decimal and percentage form?

- Does every decimal have an equivalent fraction and percentage form?

- Does every percent have an equivalent fraction and decimal form?

- How do you convert from one form to another?

- Why is it important to be able to make these conversions?

4. Types of Operations (page 4)

Objective

Students will review the four basic arithmetic operations.

Teaching Tips

This graphic organizer works well as a diagnostic tool. Ask each student to identify any problem spots in his or her use of these operations (e.g., dividing fractions). Then, work with students individually to address these areas.

Discussion Questions

- What are the four basic arithmetic operations?

- What is the purpose of each operation?

- What are some terms related to each operation?

Teaching Notes

5. Laws of Operations (page 5)

Objective

Students will define and provide the mathematical expressions of the five laws of operations.

Teaching Tips

This graphic organizer works well as a partners activity. Insist that students memorize these five laws. Encourage them to develop mnemonic devices to remember, and pair students to quiz each other on the properties.

Discussion Questions

- What is the definition of each law?

- What is the mathematical expression of each law?

- What method or methods can you use to memorize each law?

6. Order of Operations (page 6)

Objective

Students will learn and memorize the order of operations.

Teaching Tips

A traditional mnemonic acrostic is PEMDAS, and a traditional mnemonic sentence is, "Please excuse my dear Aunt Sally." Both remind students that the order of operations is: 1) parentheses, 2) exponents, 3) multiplication and division, and 4) addition and subtraction. Remind students to move from left to right at each step.

Discussion Questions

- What is the order of operations?

- How can you remember the correct order of operations?

Teaching Notes

Algebra

7. The World Is Built on Algebra (page 7)

Objective

Students will identify and investigate algebra in a macro sense, including its definition, importance, and use.

Teaching Tips

This graphic organizer works well as a whole-class activity. Make sure students understand the importance of algebra in building the world. Extend instruction by directing them to interview a professional to learn how he or she uses algebra in the office or at home. Also, use graphic organizer 42, "Six Research Questions," as needed.

Discussion Questions

- What is algebra?

- Why is algebra important?

- What are some specific ways algebra is used in everyday life?

- What is your experience with algebra?

8. Algebra Words (page 8)

Objective

Students will define several key words used in their study of algebra.

Teaching Tips

Have students write a definition, a symbol, or any other appropriate note in the space under each word. Invite them to add one or two additional terms to the graphic organizer. Encourage students to memorize the meaning of each word and to add to their graphic organizers as they learn new information that will help them remember the meanings.

Discussion Questions

- What does each word mean?

- Why is it important to memorize these terms?

Teaching Notes

9. Different Forms of Representation (page 9)

Objective

Students will compare and contrast the advantages and disadvantages of three basic forms of representation used in algebra.

Teaching Tips

Have students take a problem and create a table, graph, and equation to help them weigh the advantages and disadvantages of each form of representation. Consider having them draw three scale diagrams on the backs of their graphic organizers to weigh the advantages of each form of representation for the problem against one another (i.e., the advantages of a table against the advantages of a graph, a graph against an equation, and a table against an equation). Extend instruction by having them write paragraphs that explain why each form of representation is best for certain situations.

Discussion Questions

- What are the advantages of each form of representation? Disadvantages?

- When is each form of representation most useful? Why?

10. Roles of Variables (page 10)

Objective

Students will identify and investigate four roles that variables can perform in algebra.

Teaching Tips

Emphasize that identifying the role of a variable in a problem is one of the first steps students should take when addressing a problem. Have students develop mnemonic devices to help them remember these four roles of variables.

Discussion Questions

- What roles can variables perform?

- What are some examples of each role?

- How can you remember these four roles?

Teaching Notes

11. Linear and Nonlinear Relationships (page 11)

Objective

Students will define, compare, and contrast linear and nonlinear relationships.

Teaching Tips

Make sure students understand the proper use of a Venn diagram. Encourage them to include definitions, descriptions, examples, and other notes on their graphic organizers. Also, use graphic organizer 48, "Venn Diagram Template," as needed.

Discussion Questions

- What is a linear relationship? Nonlinear relationship?

- Why is it important to understand the differences between the two?

- What are some examples of each?

Geometry

12. The Importance of Geometry (page 12)

Objective

Students will identify and define geometry and describe how it is used in their personal lives and the larger world.

Teaching Tips

Explain to students that *etymology* is the history or origin of a word. Encourage them to list as many items as possible in the "Uses" cell, and emphasize the widespread use of geometry. For the "Personal Experience" cell, ask students to identify experiences they have had with geometry outside the classroom.

Discussion Questions

- What is geometry?

- What is the origin of the word *geometry*?

- How is geometry used?

- What personal experiences have you had with geometry, both in and out of the classroom?

Teaching Notes

13. Uses of Geometry (page 13)

Objective

Students will identify and describe how geometry is used in their homes, at school, in businesses, and in other areas of life.

Teaching Tips

Direct students to identify how geometry is used in the places identified on the graphic organizer. Encourage them to think in a progressive manner about each place; e.g., students might think about how the builders used geometry, how the creators of the objects in each building used geometry, how the people in each building might use geometry, and so on.

Discussion Questions

- How is geometry used in your home? school? work? other areas of life?

- Are you surprised that geometry is so common?

- What have you learned about the importance of geometry?

14. My Geometry Word (page 14)

Objective

Students will define and illustrate words used in their study of geometry.

Teaching Tips

Assign individual students different geometric terms. Have students use their textbooks or other resources to complete the graphic organizer. Then direct students to compile their graphic organizers into a classroom reference booklet of geometric terms.

Discussion Questions

- What is the definition of your geometry word?

- How did you learn how to illustrate it?

- How can you use the illustration to explain the meaning of the word?

Teaching Notes

15. Flat Shapes (page 15)

Objective

Students will identify, define, and describe flat shapes.

Teaching Tips

Direct students to sketch each shape in the small box on its cell. Have them add lines and cells to the graphic organizer as they learn about more shapes.

Discussion Questions

- What is the definition of each shape?
- How are each of the shapes like the other shapes? Different?

16. Solids (page 16)

Objective

Students will identify, define, and describe solids.

Teaching Tips

Direct students to sketch each solid in the small box on its cell. Have them add lines and cells to the graphic organizer as they learn about more solids.

Discussion Questions

- What is the definition of each solid?
- How are each of the solids like the other solids? Different?

Teaching Notes

17. The Pythagorean Relationship (page 17)

Objective

Students will define, formulate, and provide examples and uses of the Pythagorean relationship.

Teaching Tips

Make sure students understand the boxes in the triangles indicate right angles and therefore right triangles. Consider modeling the Pythagorean relationship with the "3-4-5" or "builder's" triangle: a right triangle of string where the sides are 3 and 4 feet long (or some other standard measurement) and the hypotenuse is 5 feet long (or some other standard measurement). Since $3^2 + 4^2 = 5^2$, the resulting triangle is a right triangle. A builder can create a right angle, essential for construction.

Discussion Questions

- What is the Pythagorean relationship?

- What do the small boxes in the triangles mean?

- What is the formula for the Pythagorean relationship?

- What are some examples and uses of the Pythagorean relationship?

Measurement

18. The Metric System (page 18)

Objective

Students will explain the metric system as a decimal system, identify its three most common base units, and discuss its use of prefixes.

Teaching Tips

This graphic organizer works well as a partners activity. Have students review the information on it together to aid memorization. Extend instruction by having them combine several prefixes with several base unit names to create metric system terms. Correct any terms that are wrong.

Discussion Questions

- What is a decimal system?

- What are the three most common base units of the metric system?

- What are the prefixes used in the metric system?

- Why is the metric system easy to remember and use?

Teaching Notes

19. English and Metric Conversions (page 19)

Objective

Students will identify and apply the techniques for metric-English and English-metric conversions.

Teaching Tips

This graphic organizer works well as a partners activity. Assign student pairs to generate conversion problems for each other and to check one another's work. Encourage student memorization of conversion techniques.

Discussion Questions

- What do you multiply by to make each conversion?

- Why do you need to know how to make these conversions?

- What can you do to remember this information?

20. English and Metric Equivalencies (page 20)

Objective

Students will identify the approximate metric equivalents of common English measurements.

Teaching Tips

This graphic organizer works well as a partners activity or as a homework assignment. Consider having students practice by going to the grocery store and estimating the metric equivalents of items sold in English units.

Discussion Questions

- Which are units of length? Area? Volume? Weight?

- What is the approximate metric equivalent of each one?

- How can this knowledge help you in everyday life?

Teaching Notes

21. Perimeter, Area, and Volume (page 21)

Objective

Students will define, compare, and contrast the concepts of perimeter, area, and volume.

Teaching Tips

Make sure students understand the proper use of a triple Venn diagram. Encourage them to include definitions, descriptions, and formulas on their graphic organizers. Extend instruction by identifying one two-dimensional and one three-dimensional object in your classroom. Have students calculate the two-dimensional object's perimeter and area. Then, have them calculate the three-dimensional object's surface area and volume. Also, use graphic organizer 49, "Triple Venn Diagram Template," as needed.

Discussion Questions

- What is perimeter? Area? Volume?

- What does each of these apply to?

- How do you find out the perimeter of various shapes and parts of shapes? Area? Volume?

Data Analysis and Probability

22. Scatter Plots (page 22)

Objective

Students will analyze the construction of a scatter plot.

Teaching Tips

Make sure students understand that the purpose of a scatter plot is to show where data points fall in relation to two variables. Point out that some people call scatter plots by different terms such as *scatter grams* or *scatter graphs*. Have students apply their knowledge of the purpose and parts of scatter plots to specific scatter plots in their textbooks.

Discussion Questions

- What is a scatter plot?

- What is the name of each part of a scatter plot? Purpose?

Teaching Notes

23. Mean, Median, and Mode (page 23)

Objective

Students will define, compare, and contrast the concepts of mean, median, and mode.

Teaching Tips

Make sure students understand the proper use of a triple Venn diagram. Encourage them to include definitions, descriptions, and formulas on their graphic organizers. Remind them to use the specific terms *mean*, *median*, and *mode* instead of the general term *average*. Also, use graphic organizer 48, "Triple Venn Diagram Template," as needed.

Discussion Questions

- What is a mean? Median? Mode?

- How are the three alike? Different?

- How do you find out mean? Median? Mode?

24. What Is Probability? (page 24)

Objective

Students will answer fundamental questions about probability and then create and answer additional questions.

Teaching Tips

Have students turn their graphic organizers over and create their own questions for each cell. Then, have the students read them aloud as a basis for class discussion. Also, use graphic organizer 42, "Six Research Questions," as needed.

Discussion Questions

- How did you respond to the questions on the graphic organizer?

- What questions did you create?

Teaching Notes

Problem Solving

25. Strategies for Solving Problems (page 25)

Objective

Students will identify and list the advantages and disadvantages of several strategies for solving problems.

Teaching Tips

Before students complete this graphic organizer, make sure they can define *problem solving strategies*. They should give the definition, "methods of approaching problems and solving them," or something similar.

Discussion Questions

- What are several strategies for solving problems?

- When should you use each one?

- What are some advantages of each strategy? Disadvantages?

26. Problem Solving Steps (page 26)

Objective

Students will identify and describe the steps in the problem solving process.

Teaching Tips

Review the steps conceptually at first or with a nonmathematical example. Then, guide students to apply the steps to a classroom problem, and have them make notes about what to do at each step in the appropriate spaces. Consider having them work independently by applying these steps to a classroom assignment. Compare and contrast students' experiences in a classroom discussion.

Discussion Questions

- What are the steps in the problem solving process?

- What should you do at each step?

Teaching Notes

27. K-W-L Chart (page 27)

Objective

Students will explain and apply a K-W-L chart.

Teaching Tips

Make sure students complete columns 1 and 2 ("K" and "W") on their graphic organizers after they look over the assignment but before they attempt it, and that they complete column 3 ("L") while they work on the assignment and after they complete it. K-W-L charts are more useful for some assignments than others and more useful for some students than others. Have students realistically evaluate their success using this graphic organizer. Typically, most students find it useful for focusing their thinking.

Discussion Questions

- What does each letter stand for?

- What are the three steps for completing a K-W-L chart?

- When should you complete each step?

28. Reflecting on Problem Solving (page 28)

Objective

Students will identify their strengths and weaknesses as problem solvers and find ways to overcome their weaknesses.

Teaching Tips

Have students use this graphic organizer to evaluate themselves as problem solvers. Respect their feelings, but encourage honest assessments. Be positive, helping students identify the steps necessary for improvement and explaining how to put those steps into action. Emphasize that they should enjoy their feelings of accomplishment. Consider having students repeat the graphic organizer after they have made improvements in order to highlight their increased knowledge, success, and skills as problem solvers.

Discussion Questions

- What are your strengths as a problem solver? Weaknesses?

- How can you become a better problem solver?

Teaching Notes

Reasoning and Proof

29. Mathematical Reasoning (page 29)

Objective

Students will identify and explain the basic steps in mathematical reasoning.

Teaching Tips

This graphic organizer works well as a whole-class activity, an enrichment exercise, or as an advanced activity for students working alone. Explain that *reasoning* is drawing conclusions from facts, and a *conjecture* is an educated guess. Challenge students to explain the statement, "Reasoning is fundamental to mathematics."

Discussion Questions

- What does each step mean?

- What is an example of how you can apply each step?

30. Deductive and Inductive Reasoning (page 30)

Objective

Students will define, compare, and contrast deductive and inductive reasoning.

Teaching Tips

This graphic organizer works well as a whole-class activity. Make sure students understand the proper use of a Venn diagram. Encourage them to apply their understanding of deductive and inductive reasoning to areas outside the classroom. Help them identify times they have used deductive or inductive reasoning in their everyday lives. Also, use graphic organizer 48, "Venn Diagram Template," as needed.

Discussion Questions

- What is deductive reasoning? Inductive reasoning?

- How are they alike? Different?

- What are some examples of each?

Teaching Notes

Communication

31. Communication Skills (page 31)

Objective

Students will list and provide examples of communication skills.

Teaching Tips

Examples of mathematical communication skills include using terms correctly, presenting information in a logical order, being a respectful listener, etc. — essentially, skills students should use in any setting. Emphasize this fact, and encourage students to apply what they know about communicating outside math class.

Discussion Questions

- What are the skills?

- Why is each skill important to learn and use?

- What is an example of this skill being used?

- What is an example of what happens when the skill is not used?

32. Different Ways to Express a Mathematical Idea (page 32)

Objective

Students will express a single mathematical idea in three different ways and compare and contrast the methods of communication.

Teaching Tips

Direct students to express the same mathematical idea in three different ways using the three circles on the graphic organizer. Use the discussion questions to focus students' attention on the benefits and drawbacks of each method of communication. Challenge them to identify instances where one form would be better than the others. Repeat the activity with different types of mathematical ideas.

Discussion Questions

- Which type of communication was easiest to create? Most difficult? Why?

- Which type of communication was easiest for someone to understand? Most difficult? Why?

- What are the advantages of communicating each way? Disadvantages?

Teaching Notes

33. Simple Steps to Effective Communication (page 33)

Objective

Students will identify, explore, and apply the steps to effective mathematical communication.

Teaching Tips

Direct students to complete the cells of the graphic organizer using complete sentences and to consider a real-world example. For instance, they might need to give you an answer, tutor a peer, or ask another student for information. Have students repeat the activity using different examples. Also, challenge them to memorize these steps or the ideas behind them and to pause before they communicate to make sure they have satisfactorily completed the steps.

Discussion Questions

- What are the steps for effective mathematical communication?

- Why is each step important?

Connections

34. Fields of Mathematics (page 34)

Objective

Students will name and explain the major fields in the study of mathematics.

Teaching Tips

Make sure students understand that mathematics, like other disciplines, is separated into different fields or specialties. Have students list these fields on one side of the "ribs" in the diagram and a brief description of the field on the other side.

Discussion Questions

- What are the fields of mathematics?

- What is the subject matter of each field?

- Why do you think mathematics is divided into fields?

Teaching Notes

35. Math Builds on Itself (page 35)

Objective

Students will describe how a mathematical concept relies on other mathematical knowledge.

Teaching Tips

Emphasize to students that math builds on itself, as seen in the pyramid. Direct them to write a concept at the top of the pyramid and then help them see how other concepts are necessary to support it. Other concepts should be noted in the lower building blocks. Repeat the activity for a variety of concepts.

Discussion Questions

- How does the concept at the top of the pyramid depend on the concepts beneath it?

- How does this show you it is important to keep up in math class?

36. Math Outside of Math Class (page 36)

Objective

Students will identify ways that math is used outside of math class.

Teaching Tips

Direct students to complete the three blank cells in each of the four categories. Have them add lines and cells to the graphic organizer as they think of different applications. Emphasize the widespread use of mathematics.

Discussion Questions

- How is math used in other school subjects? People's homes? The workplace?

- Where else is math used?

Teaching Notes

37. A Mathematics Current Event (page 37)

Objective

Students will recognize that mathematics issues are part of the news and will explore a mathematics current event in detail.

Teaching Tips

Current events to consider include scientific advances, economics reports, demographic figures, etc. After the students complete the activity, consider compiling the graphic organizers into a class book about mathematics news.

Discussion Questions

- What is the event?

- Why is it important?

- How does it relate to your study of mathematics? Your life in general?

38. A Famous Mathematician (page 38)

Objective

Students will identify the historical importance of a mathematician.

Teaching Tips

Have students choose an important mathematician to research. For the illustration section, tell them to sketch the individual, create an appropriate symbol, or show some other suitable illustration such as a formula associated with the mathematician. Encourage them to choose mathematicians from different parts of the world and various periods in history. Consider compiling students' graphic organizers into a class book. Also, use graphic organizer 42, "Six Research Questions," as needed.

Discussion Questions

- Who was the person?

- What important contributions did he or she make?

Teaching Notes

39. Banana Math (page 39)

Objective

Students will explain the role math plays during each step of the process of delivering a common product to the market.

Teaching Tips

Direct students to identify the role that math plays at each step in the process of bringing a product to the marketplace, from growing a banana (e.g., calculating the amount of fertilizer, number of workers, gas consumption of machinery, etc.) to divvying up a bunch of bananas with friends (i.e., simple fractions).

Discussion Questions

- How does math play a role at each step?

- How is this true for other products?

Representation

40. What Is Mathematical Representation? (page 40)

Objective

Students will answer fundamental questions about mathematical representation and then create and answer additional questions.

Teaching Tips

Make sure students understand that *mathematical representation* is the use of symbols, graphs, and other things to stand for mathematical ideas. For example, "+" is a symbol that represents the idea of addition. Have students turn their graphic organizers over and create their own questions for each category. Then, have them read the questions aloud as a basis for class discussion. Use graphic organizer 42, "Six Research Questions," as needed.

Discussion Questions

- How did you respond to the questions on the graphic organizer?

- What questions did you create?

Teaching Notes

41. Types of Mathematical Representation (page 41)

Objective

Students will describe types of mathematical representation and compare and contrast their advantages and disadvantages.

Teaching Tips

Work with students to help them understand when each type of representation is most useful. Challenge them to identify a type of problem for which each type of mathematical representation would be ideal.

Discussion Questions

- What are several types of mathematical representation?

- What are the advantages of each one? Disadvantages?

Additional Graphic Organizers and Templates

42. Six Research Questions (page 42)
Use on occasion to encourage deeper student exploration of a particular topic. Guide students in framing appropriate questions and answering them correctly.

43. Fraction Strips (page 43)
Use with your instruction on fractions.

44. Number Lines (page 44)
Use as needed.

45. Bar Graph Template (page 45)
Use as needed.

46. Line Graph Template (page 46)
Use as needed.

47. Circle Graph Template (page 47)
Use as needed. There are 100 spaces on the circumference.

48. Venn Diagram Template (page 48)
Use as needed. Make sure students understand the reason for the overlapping circles.

49. Triple Venn Diagram Template (page 49)
Use as needed. Make sure students understand the reason for the overlapping circles.

1. Types of Numbers

Name	
Definition	
When used	

Name	
Definition	
When used	

Name	
Definition	
When used	

Types of Numbers

Name	
Definition	
When used	

Name	
Definition	
When used	

Name	
Definition	
When used	

2. Large Numbers

Number Word	Number of Zeroes	Scientific Notation	Numeral
million			
billion			
trillion			
quadrillion			
quintillion			
sextillion			
septillion			
octillion			
nonillion			
decillion			
undecillion			
duodecillion			
tredecillion			
quattuordecillion			
quindecillion			
sexdecillion			
septendecillion			
octodecillion			
novemdecillion			
vigintillion			
googol			
centillion			
googolplex			

3. Equivalencies of Fractions, Decimals, and Percents

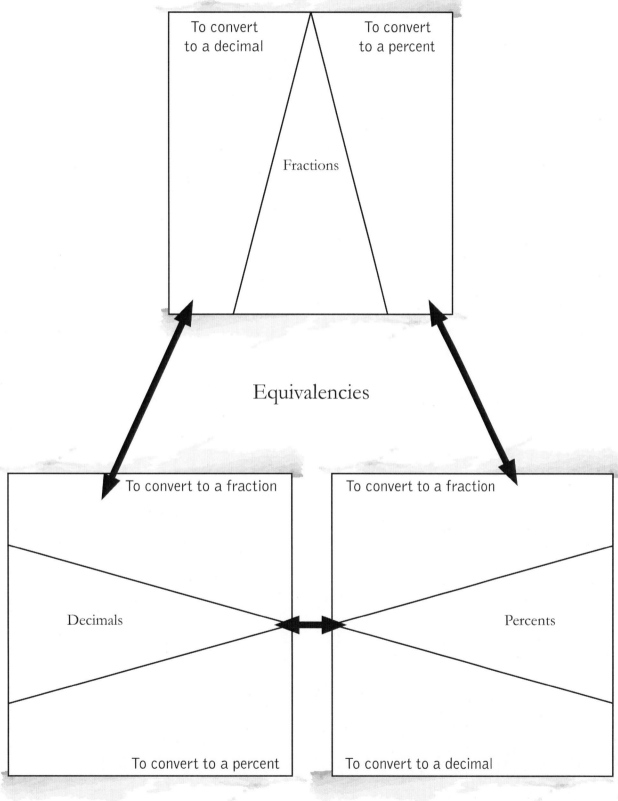

To convert to a decimal

To convert to a percent

Fractions

Equivalencies

To convert to a fraction

To convert to a fraction

Decimals

Percents

To convert to a percent

To convert to a decimal

NAME DATE

4. Types of Operations

Arithmetic Operations

+

Name

Purpose

Related Terms

−

Name

Purpose

Related Terms

×

Name

Purpose

Related Terms

÷

Name

Purpose

Related Terms

5. Laws of Operations

The Five Laws of Operations		
Law	**Definition**	**Mathematical Expression**
I. The Commutative Law of Addition		
II. The Associative Law of Addition		
III. The Commutative Law of Multiplication		
IV. The Associative Law of Multiplication		
V. The Distributive Law of Multiplication Over Addition		

6. Order of Operations

Name(s) of Operation(s)	Symbol(s)	First Letter(s) of Name(s) of Operation(s)	Word(s) That Start(s) With First Letter(s)
1.			
2.			
3.			
4.			

NAME DATE

7. The World Is Built on Algebra

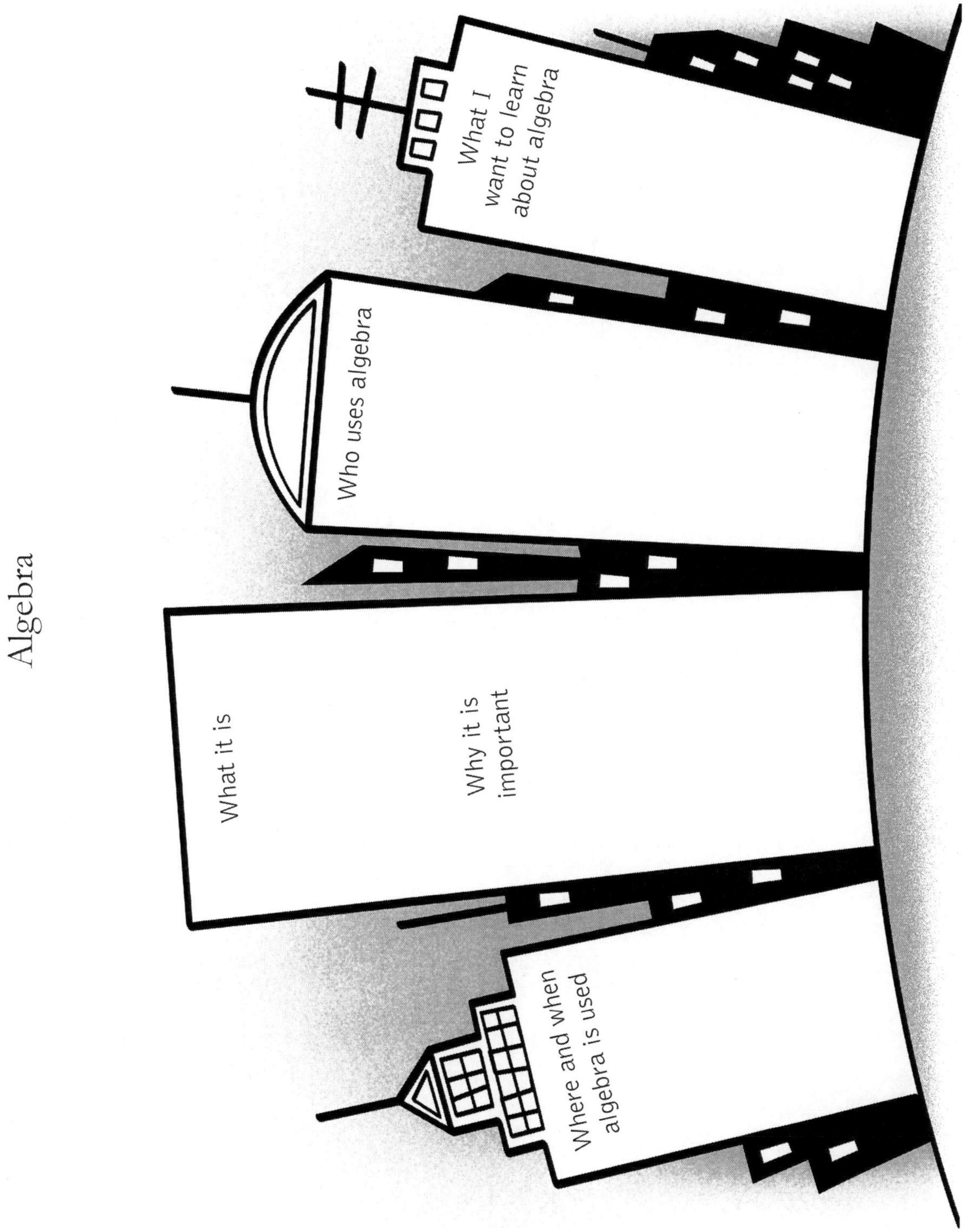
Algebra
What it is
Why it is important
Where and when algebra is used
Who uses algebra
What I want to learn about algebra

8. Algebra Words

Binomial	Coefficient	Constant

Equation	Exponent	Expression

Factors	Monomial	Polynomial

Quadratic	Root	Term

Variable	_____	_____

© 2019 SunflowerEducation.net

9. Different Forms of Representation

Weighing the Advantages and Disadvantages
of Different Forms of Representation

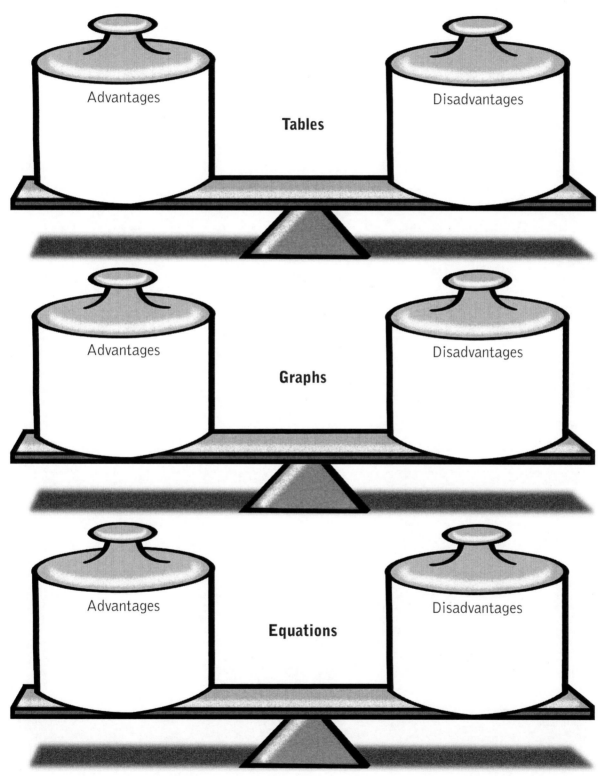

10. Roles of Variables

The Versatile Variable		
The variable can …	Example 1	Example 2
be a placeholder		
show an arithmetic pattern		
express a formula		
show covariation		

11. Linear and Nonlinear Relationships

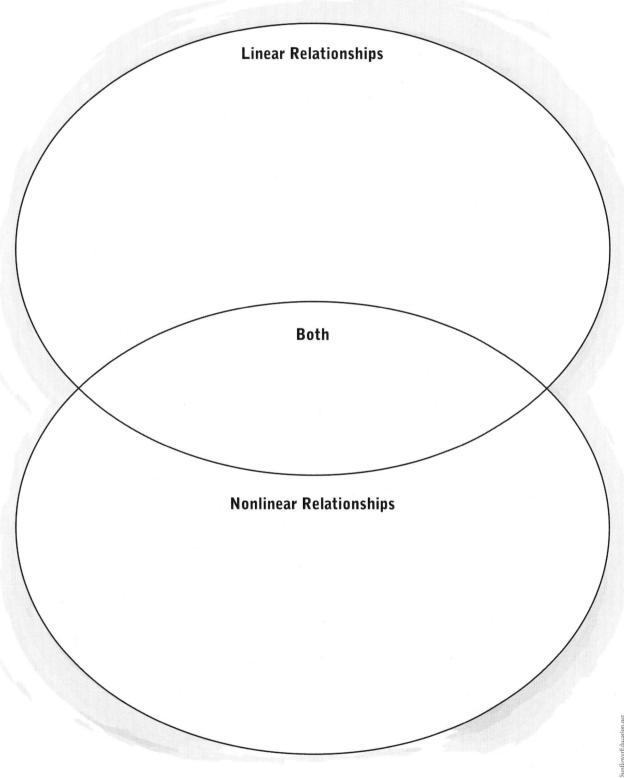

Linear Relationships

Both

Nonlinear Relationships

12. The Importance of Geometry

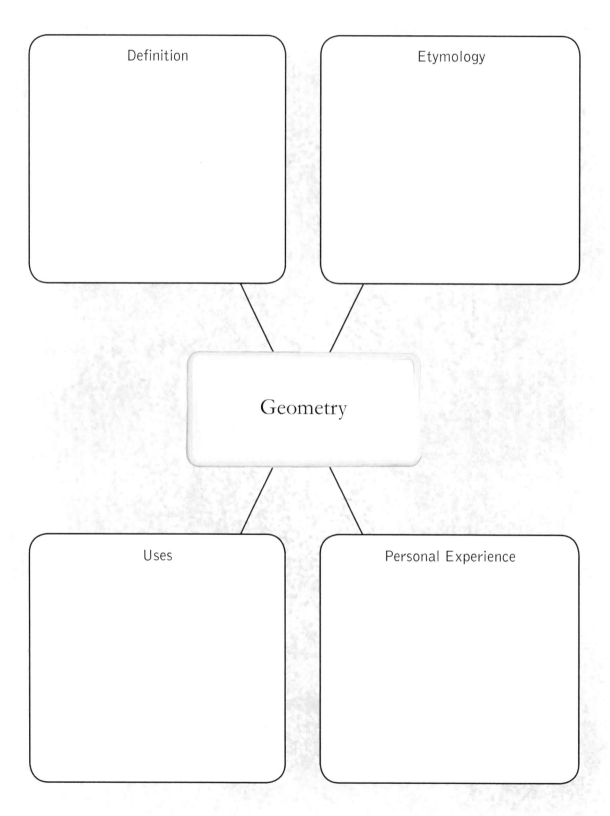

Definition

Etymology

Geometry

Uses

Personal Experience

13. Uses of Geometry

Home

School

Work

Other

14. My Geometry Words

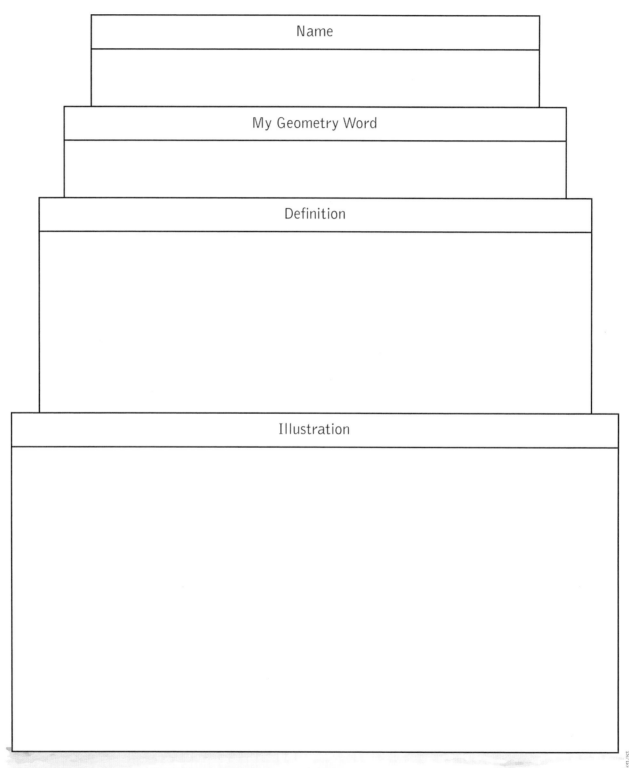

15. Flat Shapes

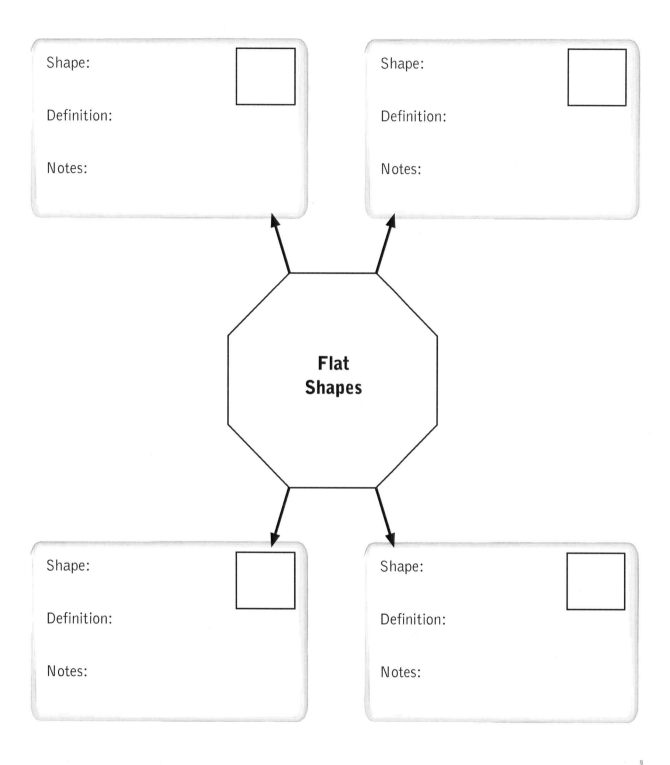

16. Solids

Solid: ☐

Definition:

Notes:

Solid: ☐

Definition:

Notes:

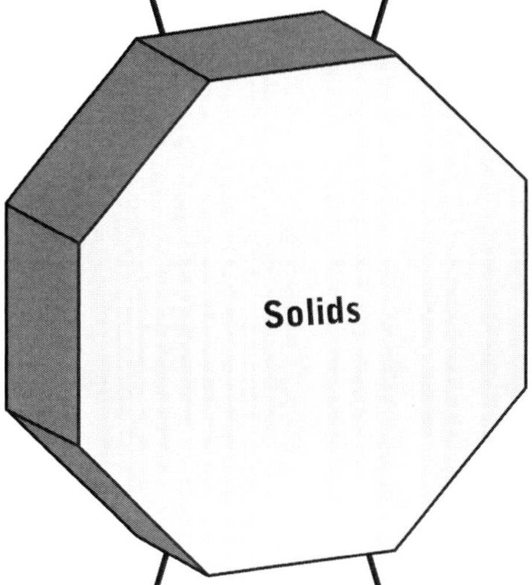

Solids

Solid: ☐

Definition:

Notes:

Solid: ☐

Definition:

Notes:

17. The Pythagorean Relationship

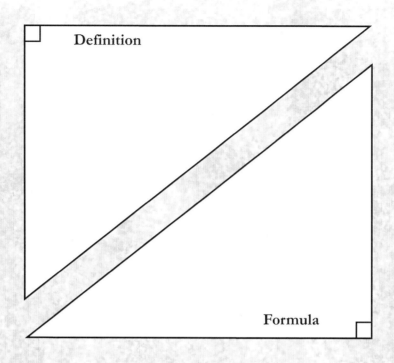

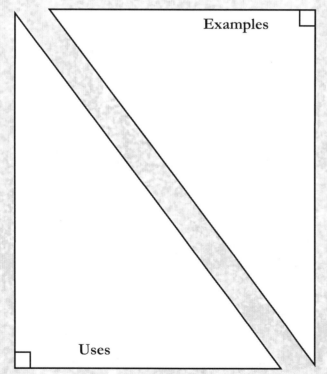

18. The Metric System

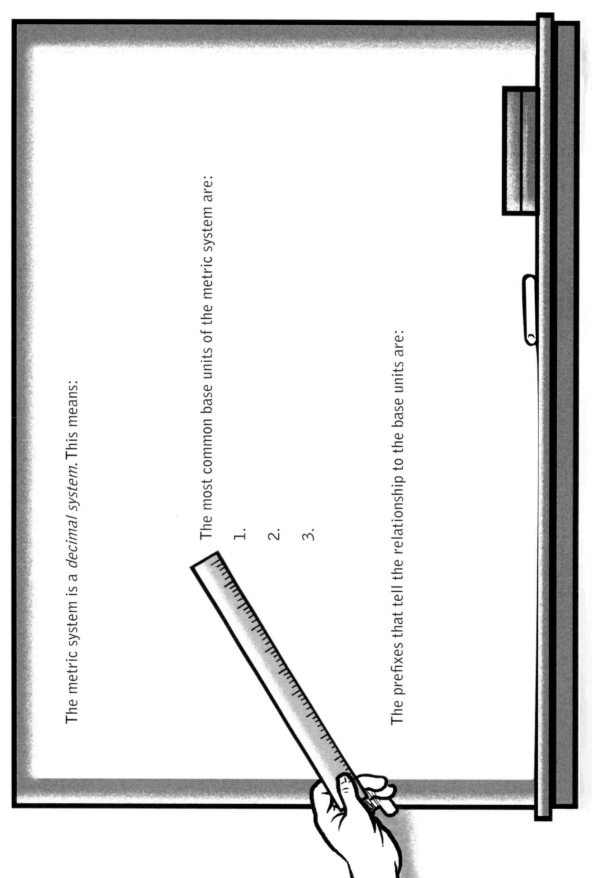

The metric system is a *decimal system*. This means:

The most common base units of the metric system are:

1.

2.

3.

The prefixes that tell the relationship to the base units are:

19. English and Metric Conversions

Metric Conversion Table		
Length and Distance		
When You Know	Multiply by	to Get
Area		
When You Know	Multiply by	to Get
Volume		
When You Know	Multiply by	to Get
Weight		
When You Know	Multiply by	to Get

20. English and Metric Equivalencies

This ...		this.
one inch	≈	_____ centimeters
one foot	≈	_____ centimeters
one yard	≈	_____ meter
one mile	≈	_____ kilometers
one square inch	≈	_____ square centimeters
one square foot	≈	_____ square meter
one square mile	≈	_____ square kilometers
one acre	≈	_____ hectare
one ounce	≈	_____ milliliters
one pint	≈	_____ liter
one quart	≈	_____ liter
one gallon	≈	_____ liters
one ounce	≈	_____ grams
one pound	≈	_____ kilogram
one ton	≈	_____ metric ton

21. Perimeter, Area, and Volume

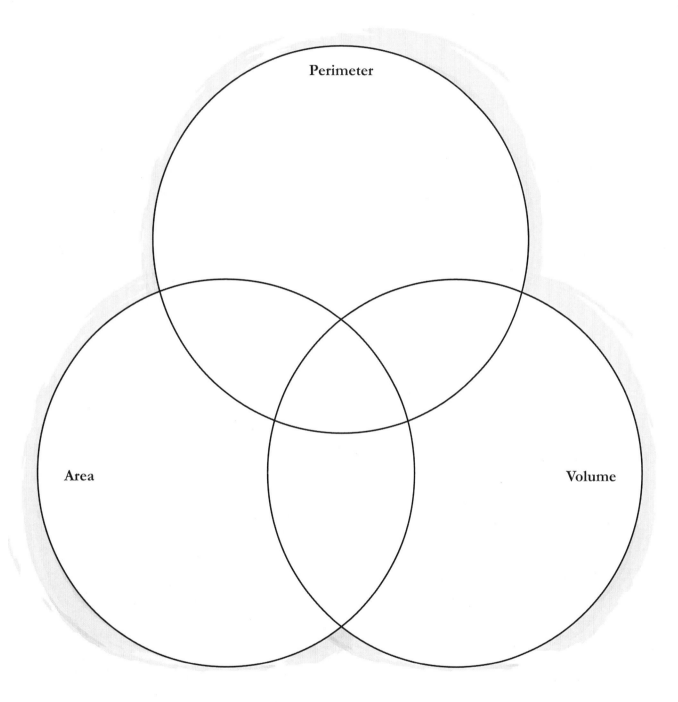

22. Scatter Plots

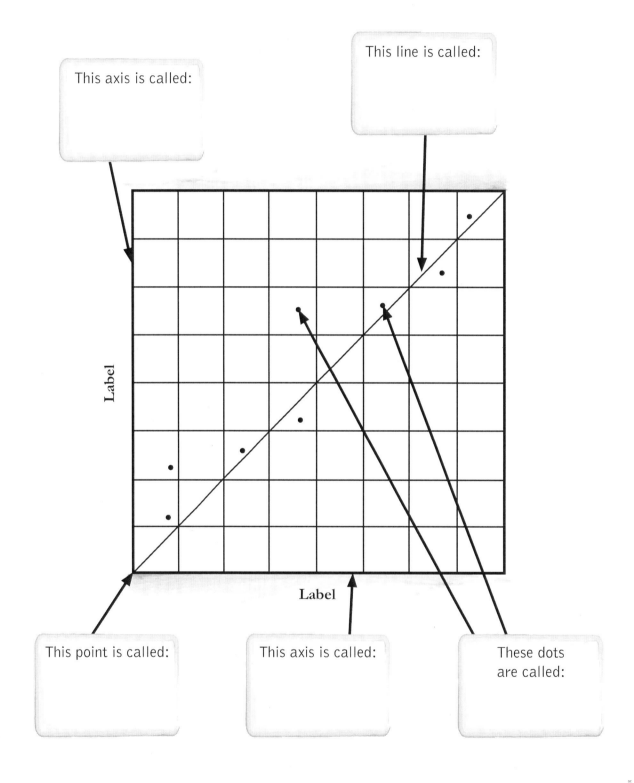

This axis is called:

This line is called:

Label

Label

This point is called:

This axis is called:

These dots are called:

23. Mean, Median, and Mode

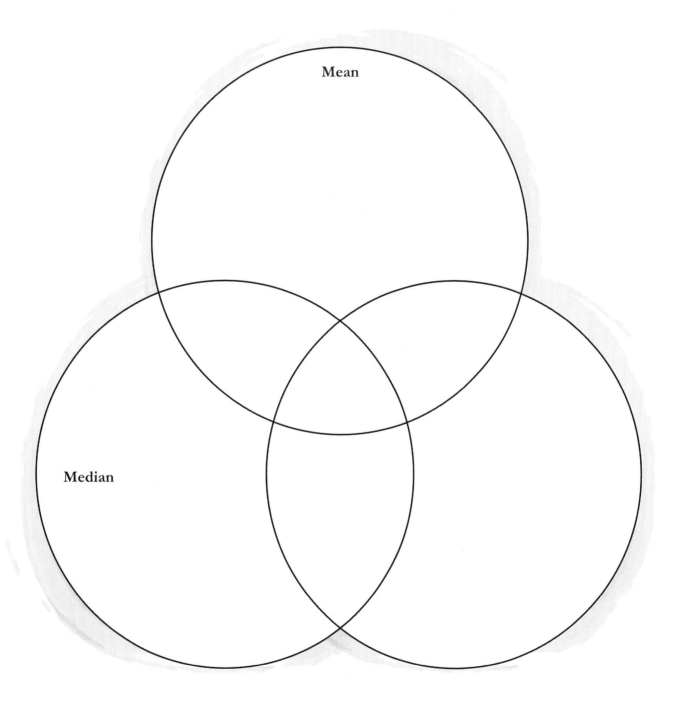

24. What Is Probability?

Who?
Who needs to know about probability?

When might you need to understand probability?

What?
What is probability?

Why?
Why is probability important?

Where can you see probability referred to every day?

How is probability a part of everyday life?

25. Strategies for Solving Problems

Problem solving strategies are:		
Strategy	Advantages	Disadvantages

GRAPHIC ORGANIZERS – MATH

© 2019 SunflowerEducation.net

26. Problem Solving Steps

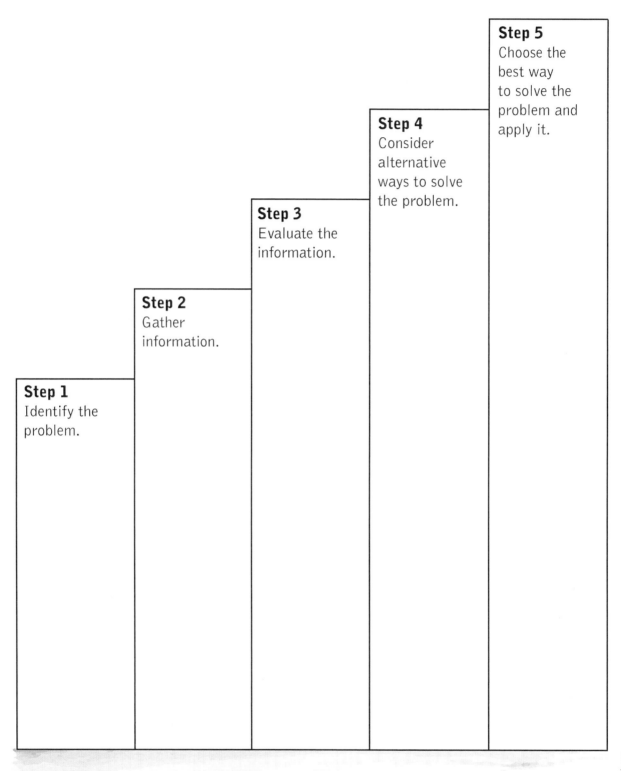

Step 1
Identify the problem.

Step 2
Gather information.

Step 3
Evaluate the information.

Step 4
Consider alternative ways to solve the problem.

Step 5
Choose the best way to solve the problem and apply it.

© 2019 SunflowerEducation.net

27. K-W-L Chart

Topic:

What I already Know	What I Want to learn	What I did Learn

28. Reflecting on Problem Solving

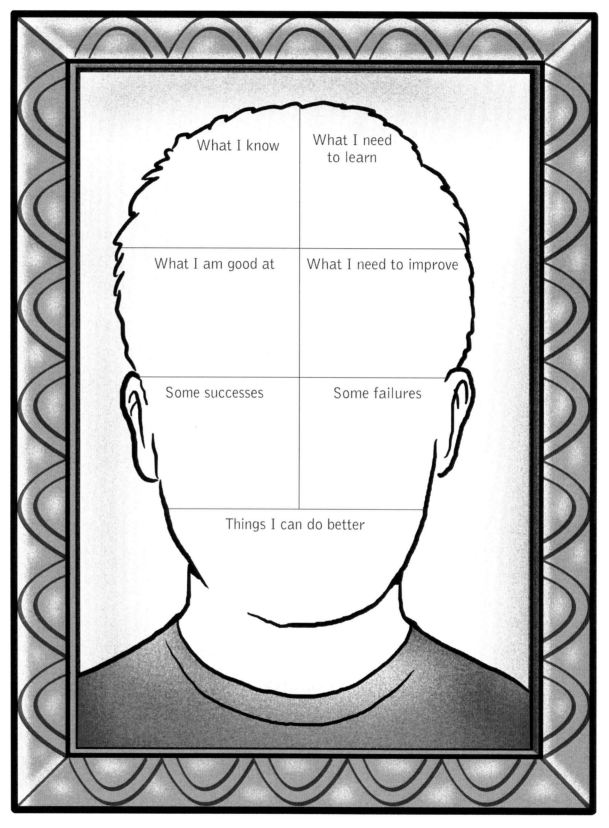

What I know

What I need
to learn

What I am good at

What I need to improve

Some successes

Some failures

Things I can do better

29. Mathematical Reasoning

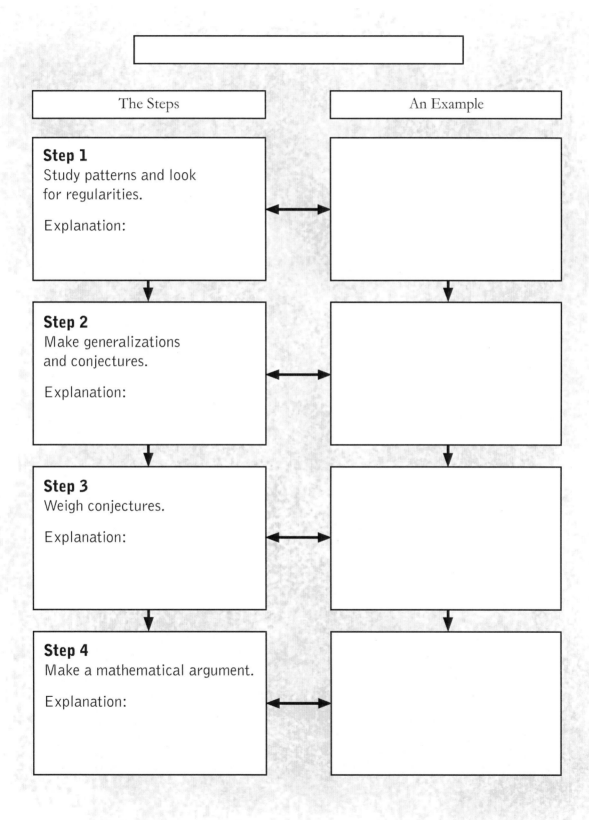

The Steps	An Example
Step 1 Study patterns and look for regularities. Explanation:	
Step 2 Make generalizations and conjectures. Explanation:	
Step 3 Weigh conjectures. Explanation:	
Step 4 Make a mathematical argument. Explanation:	

30. Deductive and Inductive Reasoning

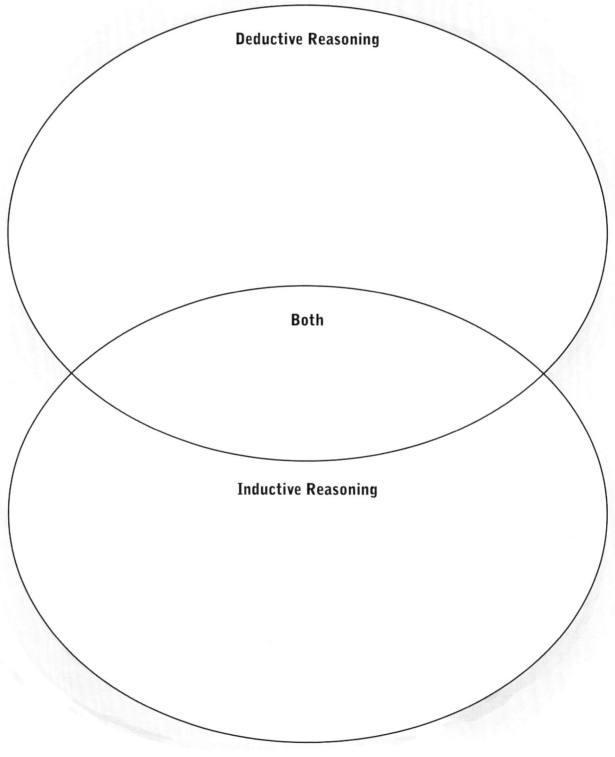

31. Communication Skills

Skill	Why This Skill Is Important	Example of the Skill Being Used	Example of What Happens When the Skill Is Not Used

32. Different Ways to Express a Mathematical Idea

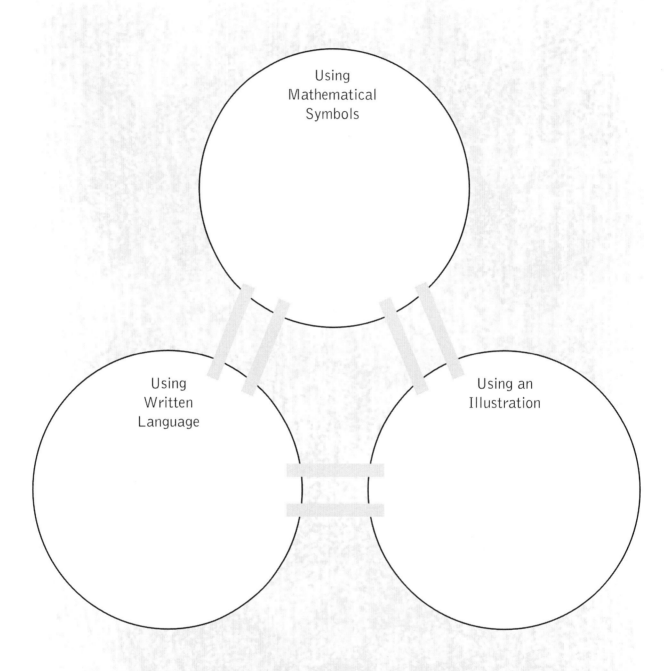

33. Simple Steps to Effective Communication

1. **What** do you want to communicate?

2. **Why** do you want to communicate it?

3. **Who** do you want to communicate it to?

4. **When** would be the best time to communicate with this person or group?

5. **How** can you best communicate what you want?

34. Fields of Mathematics

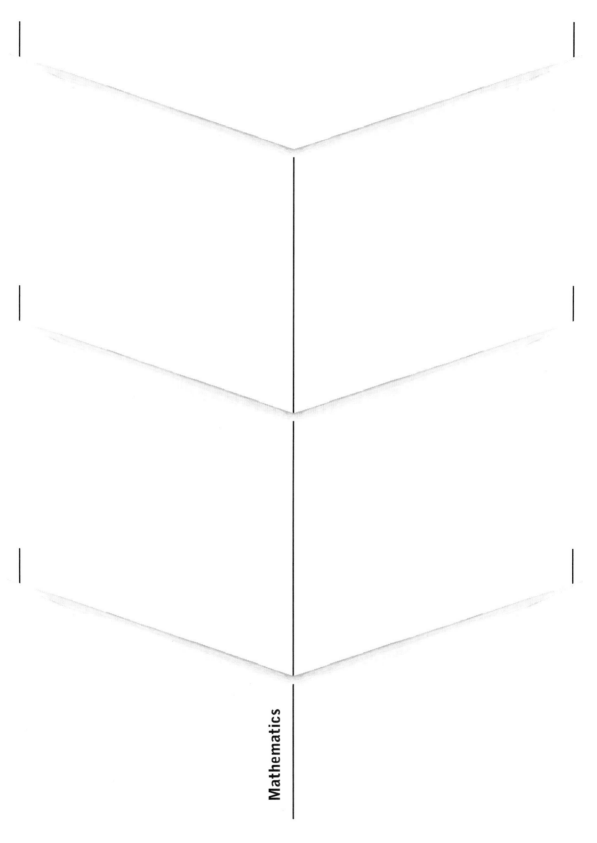

Mathematics

GRAPHIC ORGANIZERS – MATH

35. Math Builds on Itself

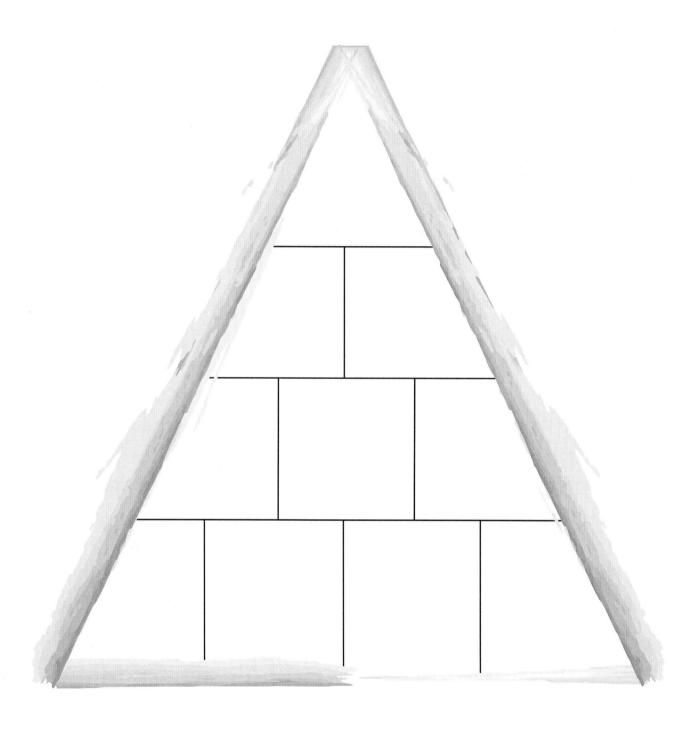

36. Math Outside of Math Class

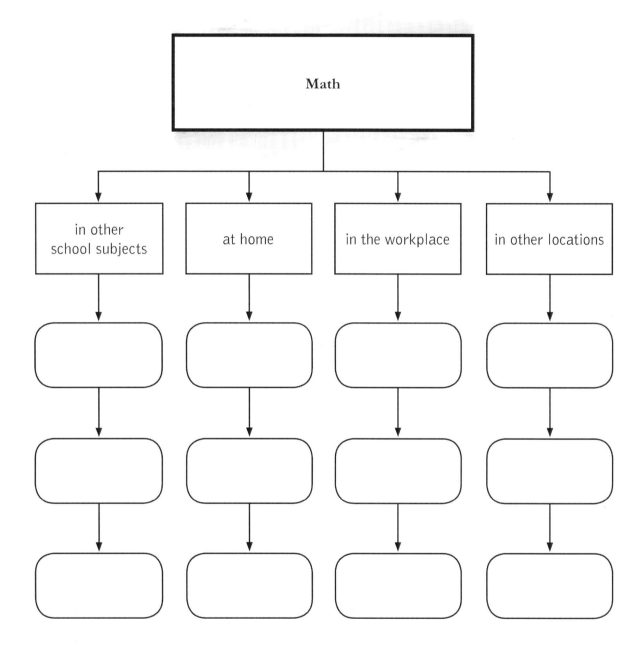

37. A Mathematics Current Event

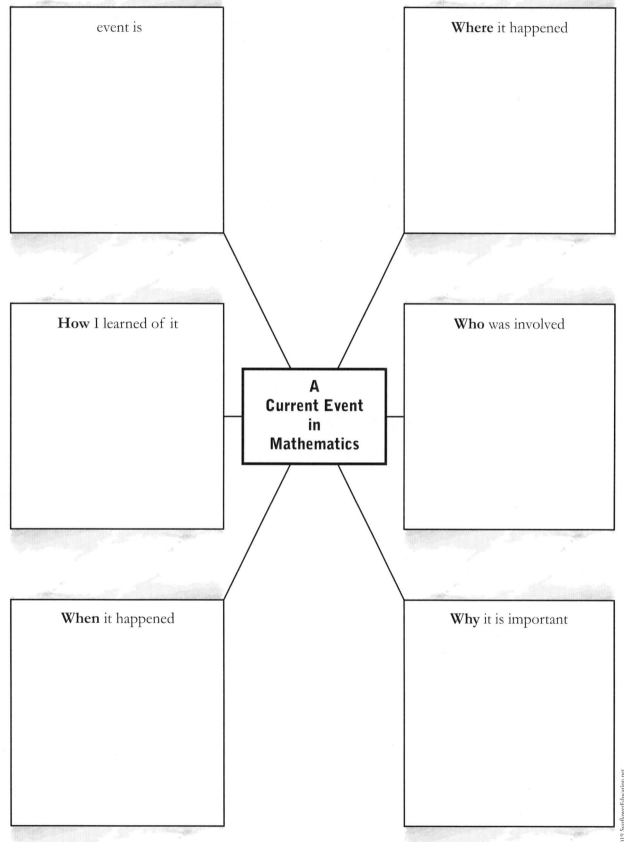

event is

Where it happened

How I learned of it

A Current Event in Mathematics

Who was involved

When it happened

Why it is important

38. A Famous Mathematician

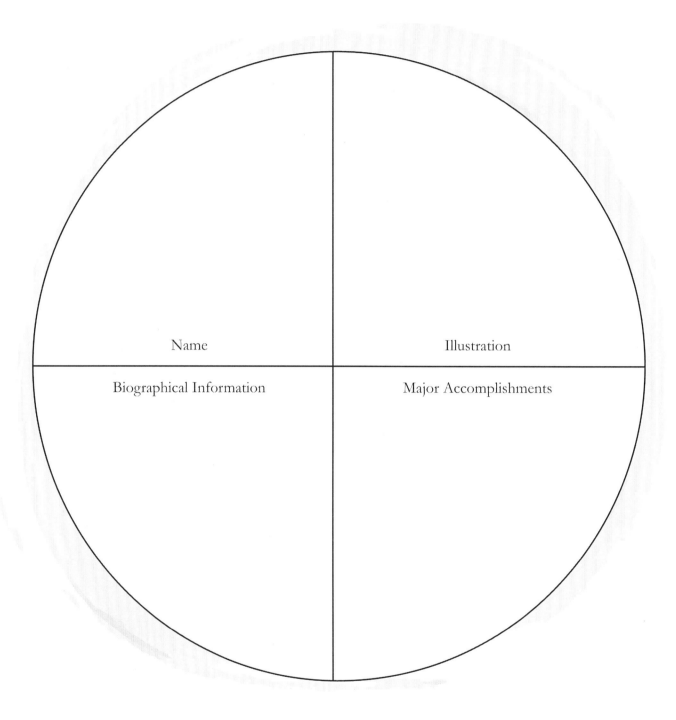

Name

Illustration

Biographical Information

Major Accomplishments

GRAPHIC ORGANIZERS – MATH

39. Banana Math

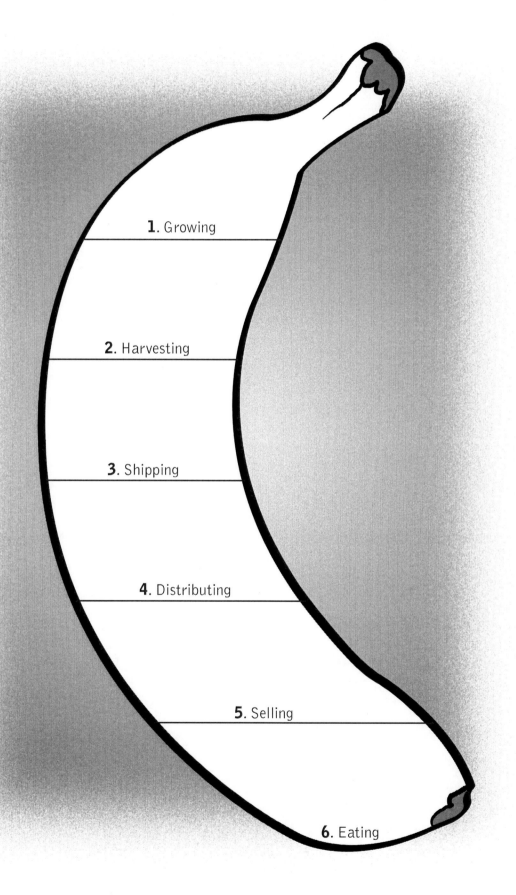

1. Growing

2. Harvesting

3. Shipping

4. Distributing

5. Selling

6. Eating

40. What Is Mathematical Representation?

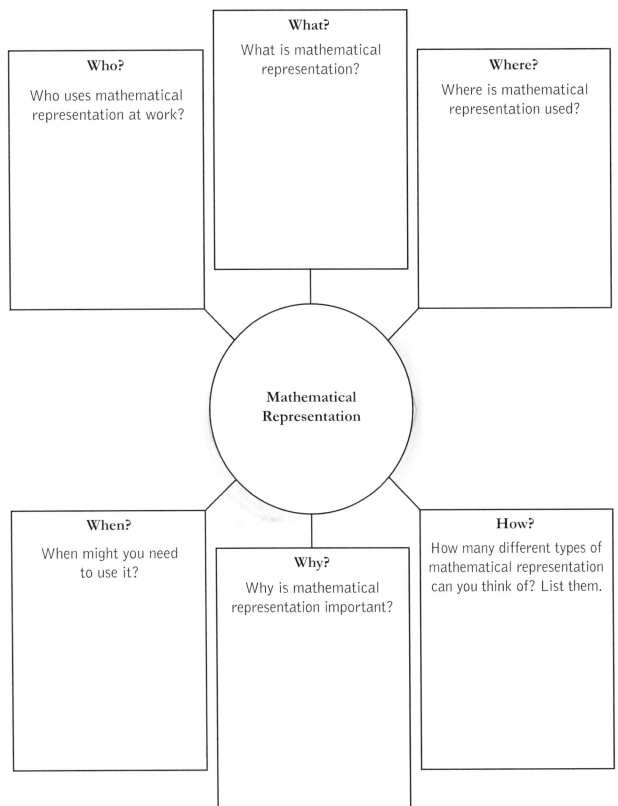

41. Types of Mathematical Representation

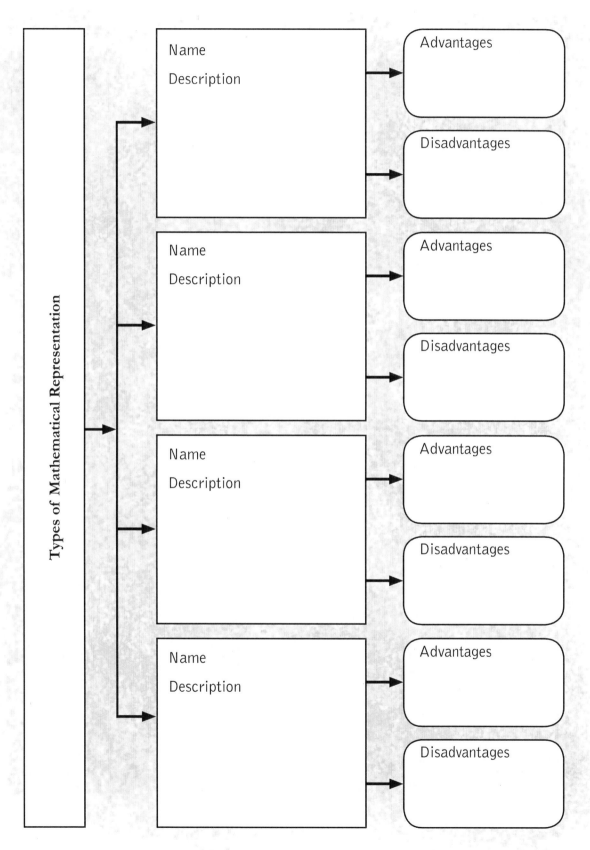

42. Six Research Questions

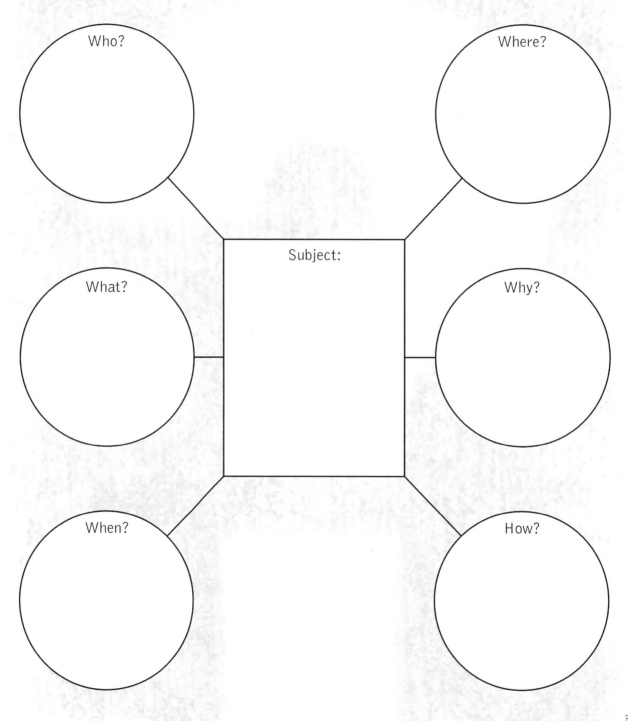

43. Fraction Strips

$$\frac{4}{4}$$

$$\frac{8}{8}$$

$$\frac{16}{16}$$

$$\frac{32}{32}$$

GRAPHIC ORGANIZERS – MATH

44. Number Lines

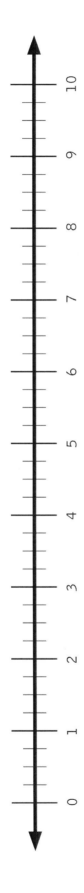

NAME DATE

45. Bar Graph Template

(title)

Key

46. Line Graph Template

_____

(title)

Key

NAME DATE

47. Circle Graph Template

____

(title)

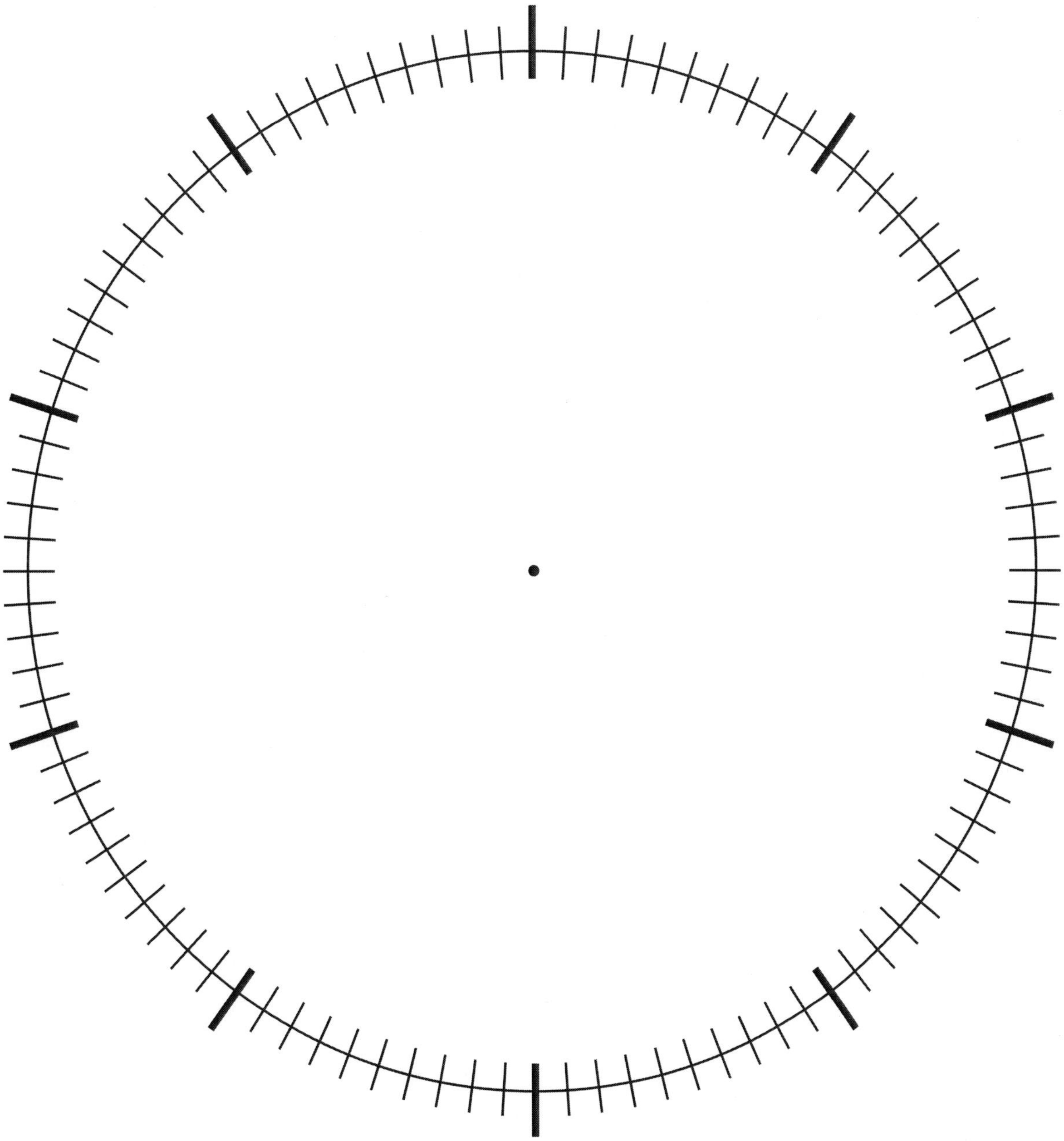

48. Venn Diagram Template

_____
(title)

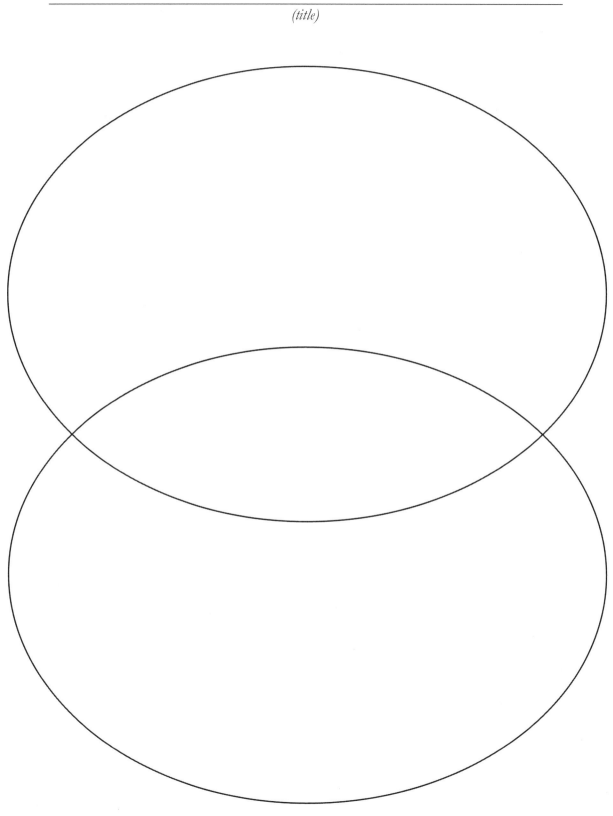

49. Triple Venn Diagram Template

_____

(title)

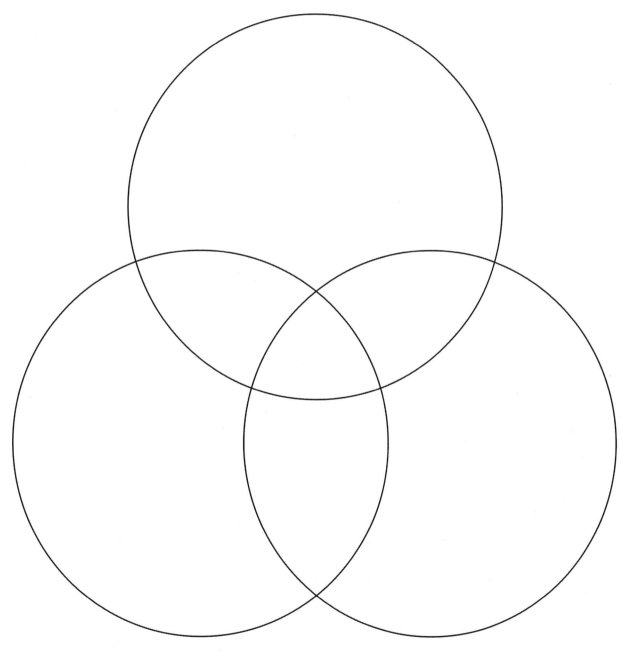

GRAPHIC ORGANIZERS – MATH

Made in United States
North Haven, CT
15 October 2021